S0-AHF-484

Fish Tales
Battle of the Barracuda

Written by Debbie Jones
Illustrated by Jodie Tucker

Fish Tales – Battle of the Barracuda is the collaborative effort of best friends Debbie Jones and Jodie Tucker

"The most beautiful discovery true friends make is that they can grow separately without growing apart."
- Elizabeth Foley

Published by Harrisii Publishing Limited

Special thanks to Richard Woolnough of Bespoke Solutions Ltd.

jonesfamily@northrock.bm
jodie.tucker@googlemail.com

Bermuda Library
ISBN 978-1-926609-90-4

Printed in China by Sure Print & Design

Fish Tales
Battle of the Barracuda

Debbie Jones
Jodie Tucker

The Battle of the Barracuda takes place at North Rock which is a coral reef off Bermuda.

North Rock

North Rock is Bermuda's largest and best known coral reef. It was originally a land mass which was visible above the surface until the beginning of the twentieth century. However, as the sea level rose it was transformed into a beautiful shallow reef.It is a great place to snorkel or dive, not only for its natural beauty with purple sea fans, yellow flowers and colourful fish, but also because it is possible to stand in certain areas. The fish at North Rock are very friendly, follow you around and are not in the least bit afraid. They almost seem to put on a show, entertaining visitors with their many antics.

North Rock is about 7 miles from the East end of Bermuda and 20 miles from the West. It is part of the most northerly chain of coral reefs in the world. The Bermuda Aquarium, Museum & Zoo has a wonderful replica exhibit so that those unable to witness North Rock first hand can have a glimpse of what it is like.

This book is dedicated to
Denise Sheridan
"Well who'd have thought"

North Rock is the name of a large coral reef
Once seen to be land, it now lies beneath
Washed by the warm salty sea, crystal and clear
A haven of peace for all who live here

Parrot fish scrape off algae, red, brown and green
Like underwater dentists, they keep the reef clean
The dance of the sea fans with eight feathery arms
Delight all who swim by with their deep purple charms

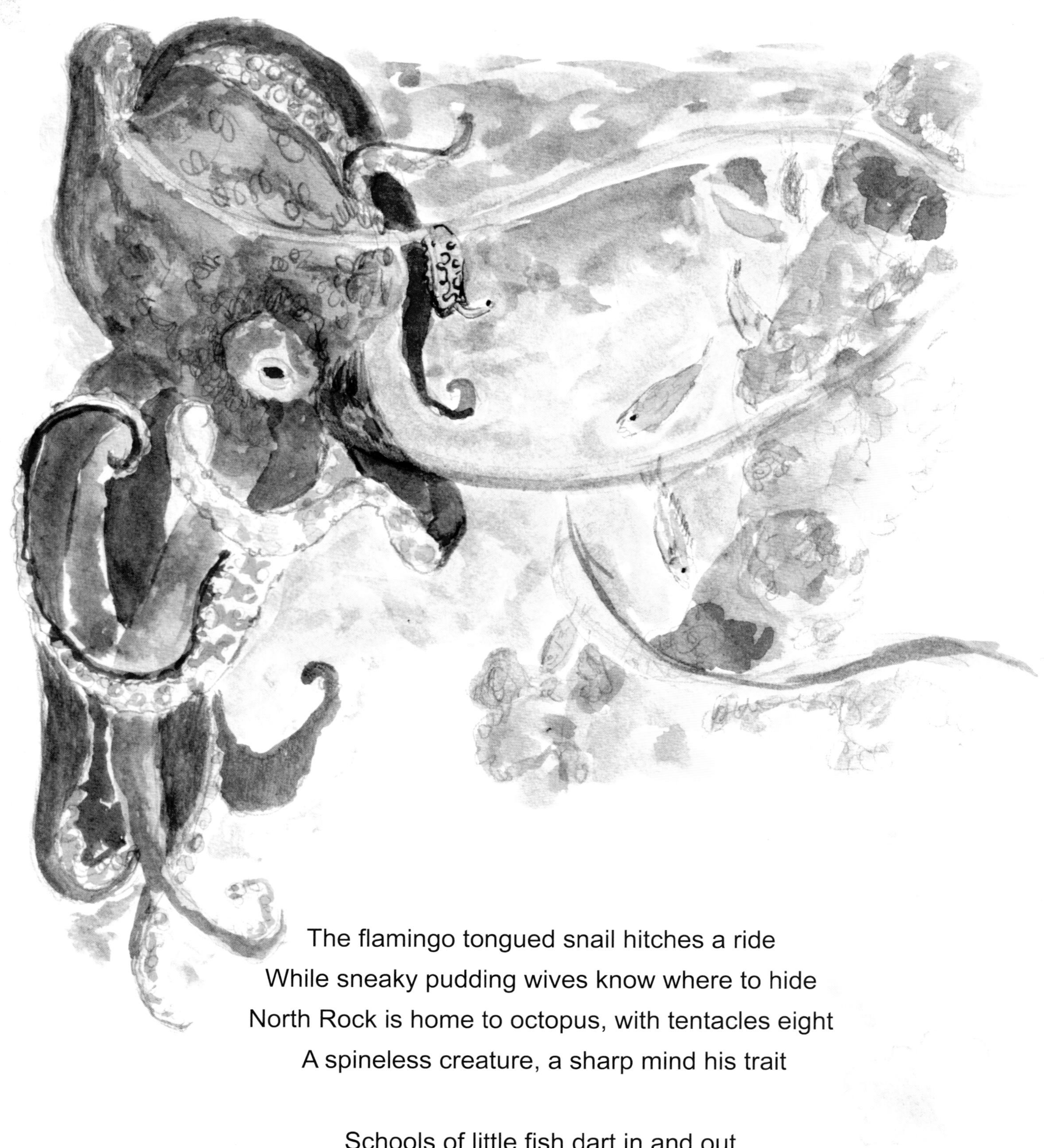

The flamingo tongued snail hitches a ride
While sneaky pudding wives know where to hide
North Rock is home to octopus, with tentacles eight
A spineless creature, a sharp mind his trait

Schools of little fish dart in and out
Sponges and seaweeds grow all about
Eels, like big snakes, emerge at night
They slither and slide, a fearsome sight

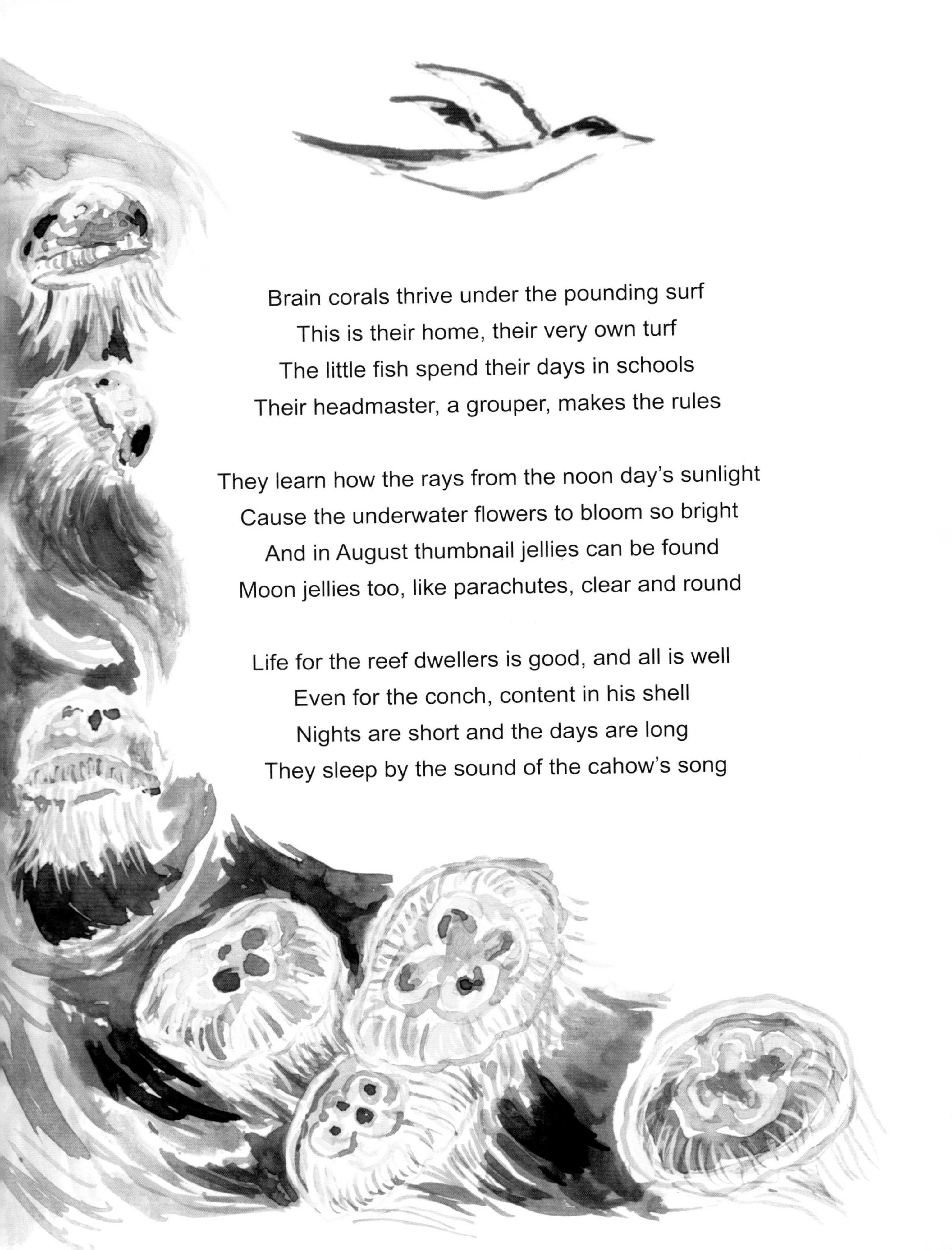

Brain corals thrive under the pounding surf
This is their home, their very own turf
The little fish spend their days in schools
Their headmaster, a grouper, makes the rules

They learn how the rays from the noon day's sunlight
Cause the underwater flowers to bloom so bright
And in August thumbnail jellies can be found
Moon jellies too, like parachutes, clear and round

Life for the reef dwellers is good, and all is well
Even for the conch, content in his shell
Nights are short and the days are long
They sleep by the sound of the cahow's song

A wise old rockfish is leader of the shoal
He keeps watch over the reef, that is his role
Home to Freddie, a wrasse, and Sam, a bream
The best of friends, they make a great team

The two little fish had been in trouble before
When on a trip to their cousins, close to shore
Mother said there will be no adventures this year
“You are going to be safe, we’ll stay right here”

Then one morning rumour spreads fast, causing alarm
"The barracuda are here," whispers the conch, "whom will they harm?"
The parrot fish passes on the news, "the bullies, they're back"
"Oh no!" says the cow polly, striped yellow and black

They shivered with fear because all had belief
Barracuda were the enemy with razor sharp teeth
Long, sleek and silvery, alone they swam
Searching for victims like Freddie and Sam

Mother said "children, you must NOT go outside
Quick off to your rooms, right now, go and hide"
Rockfish commanded trumpet fish to sound the alarm
"Remember everyone those barracuda mean harm"

For the next two days they did as Mother said
But they became oh so bored, just lying in bed
They felt like prisoners locked up in their hole
The barracuda had changed everything at North Rock shoal

Freddie put on his thinking cap and came up with a plan
"This will work Sam, at least I think it can"
"We shall need all the help we can get" said Sam
"From the fish, eels, turtles, even you little clam"

Rockfish called a meeting to recruit volunteers
"Gather round everyone, lend me your ears"
Freddie began to tell them how to defend their reef
"I can help" said a parrot fish, baring her teeth

“We shall need everyone’s help” said the little wrasse Freddie
“To defeat the barracuda we all must be ready”
They nodded in agreement and then speaking as one
“This plan will scare off the barracuda and have them on the run”

“First summon the turtles and the squid with their ink
They will be a big help” said a seahorse, her tail in a kink
“We must not forget the sea urchins and also the rays
Who can usually be found in the inland bays”

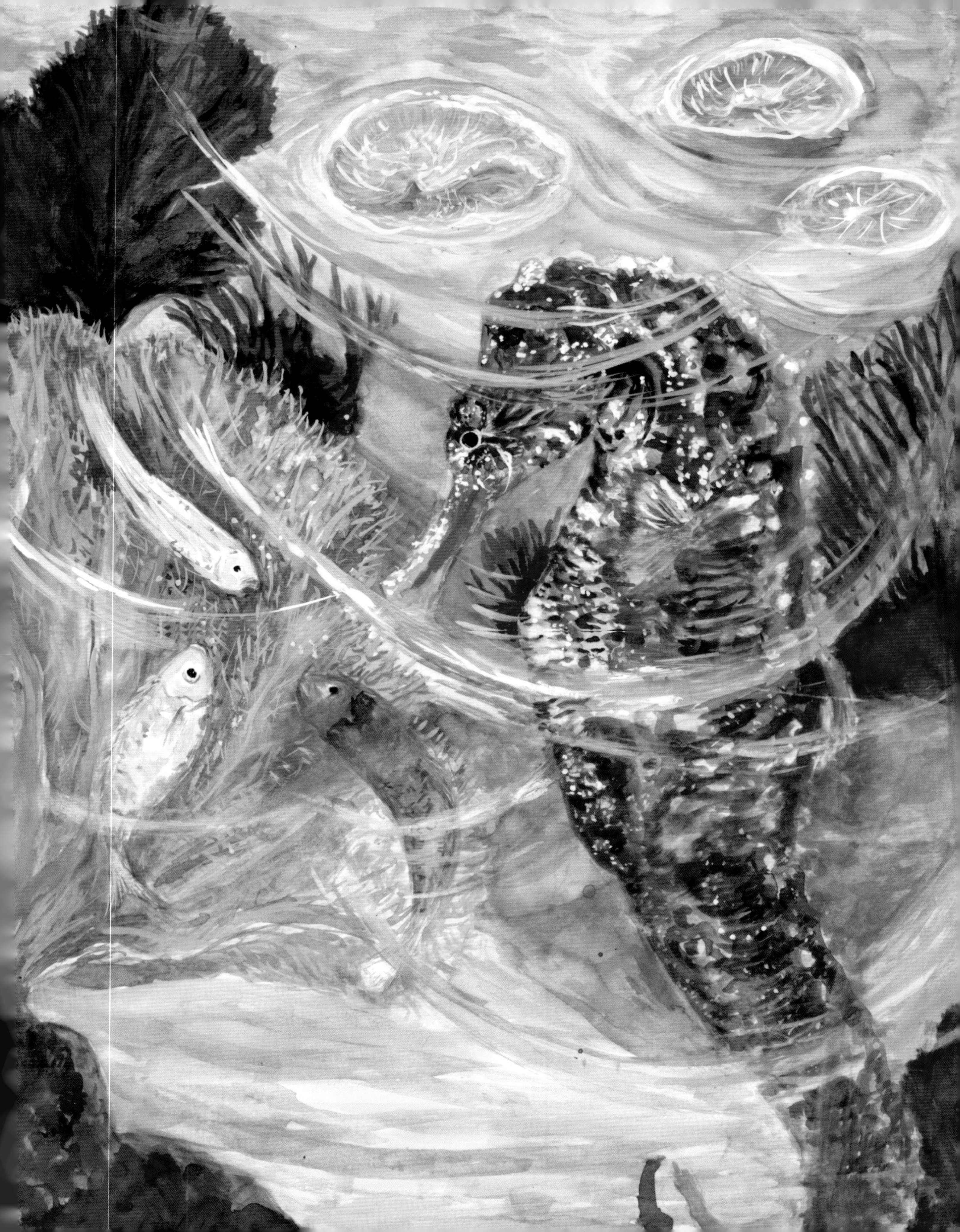

The rays answered the call and left the shore
Their wings opened wide they began to soar
Towards North Rock where the octopus had turned white
“The rays are coming” shouted Freddie, clapping his fins in delight

The turtles arrived next with some squid in tow
“Don’t forget me” said the conch “even if I am a bit slow”
“That’s fine” said Freddie “we have more work to do
We all want to be prepared for you know who

Sea urchins you can start making a barrier, a prickly wall”
“Oh do be careful” wailed mother “now please, no one fall”
At last they were ready for the fight of their life
“I can help” said the conch “my razor’s as sharp as a knife”

Each of the fish was given an important job
Mother was frightened and fought back a sob
Phyllis, a striped grunt, offered to act as a lure
“The barracuda will attack” said Freddie “that’s for sure”

Phyllis was trembling but tried hard to be brave
Freddie gave her the nod and she emerged from the cave
The barracuda swam in and went straight for the fish
Please everyone do your job was Freddie's wish

The barracuda turned and then made ready to pounce
Up went the squid's tendrils in a ballet like flounce
The inky water caused the barracuda to lose their sight
The ink from the squid had turned day into night

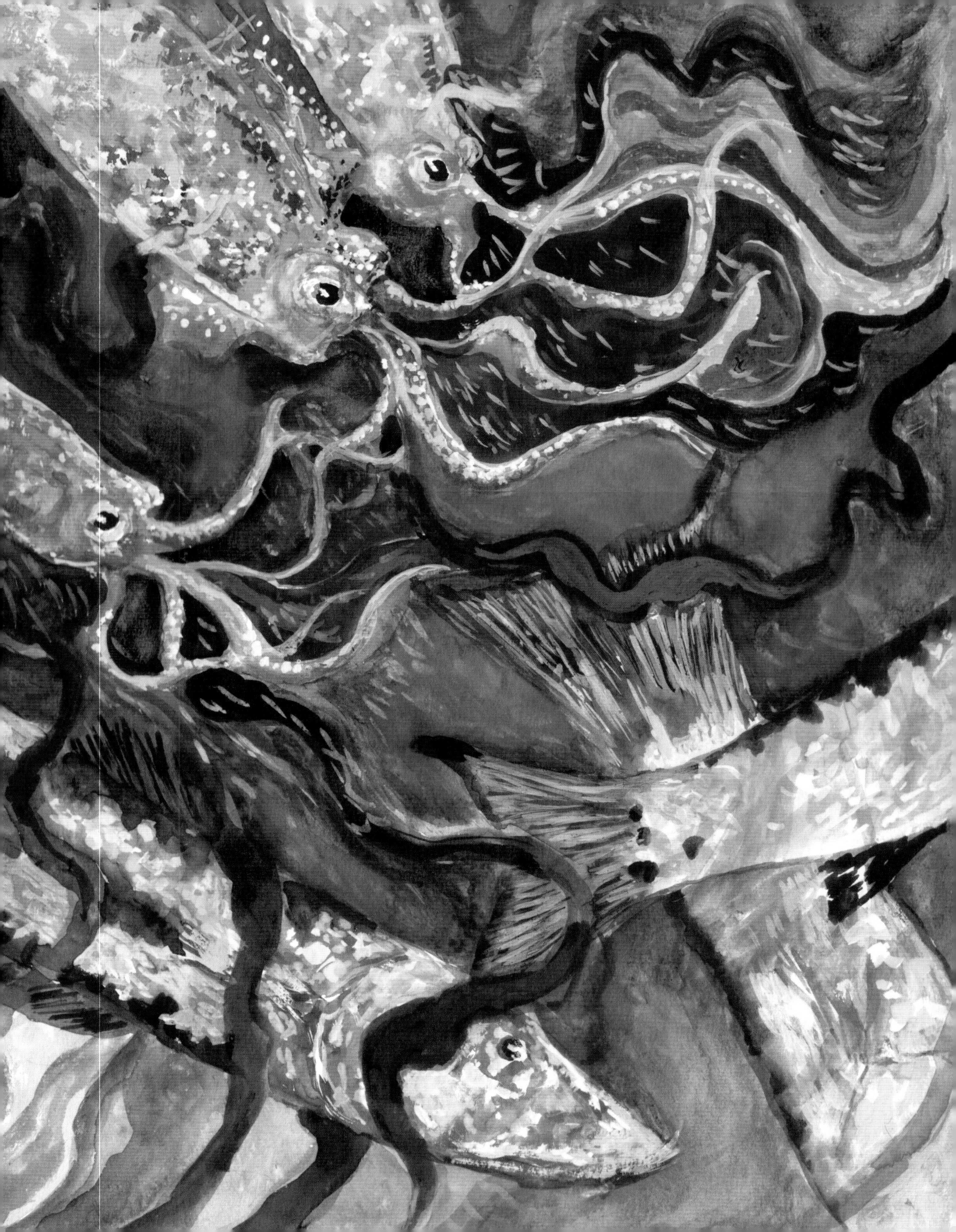

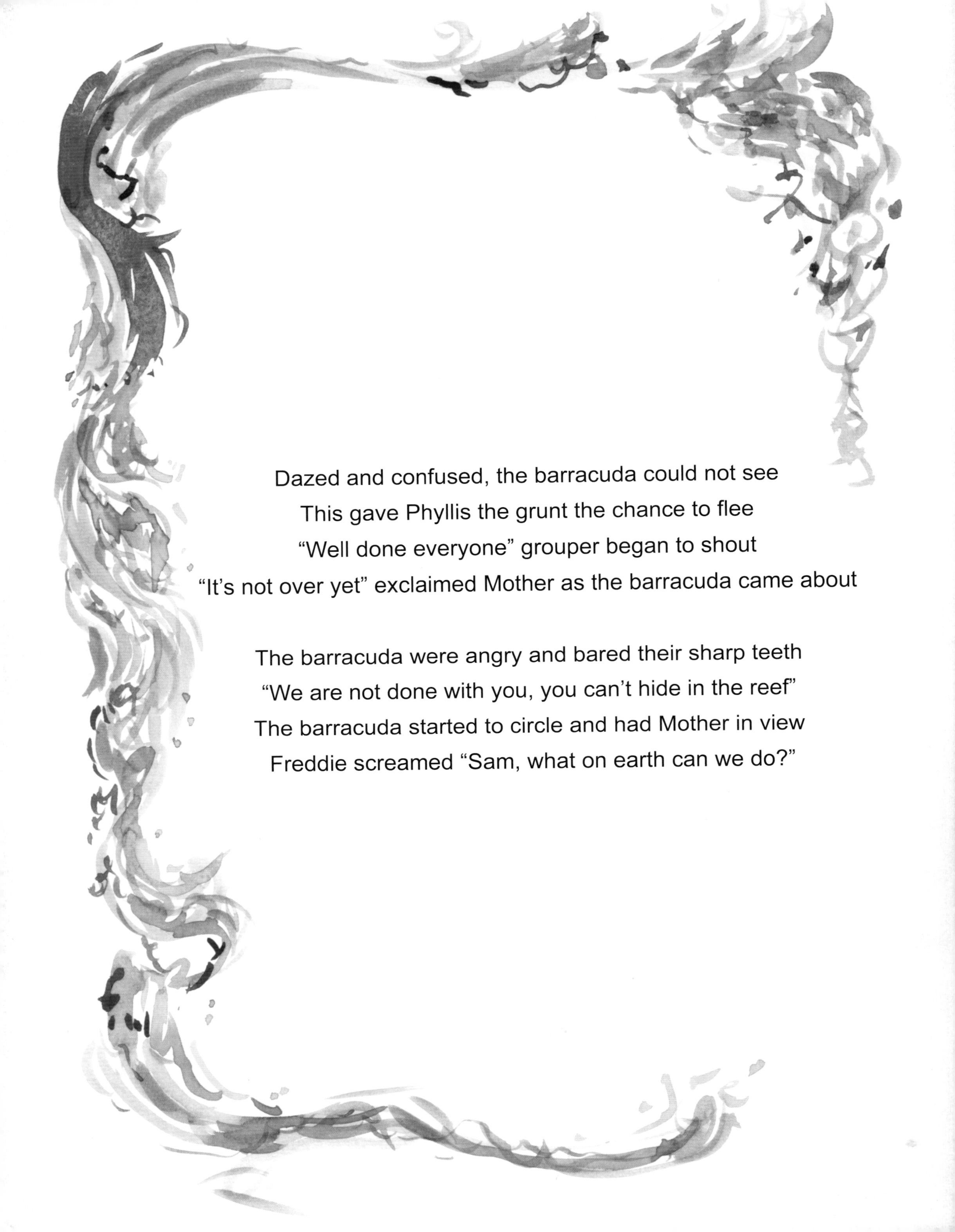

Dazed and confused, the barracuda could not see
This gave Phyllis the grunt the chance to flee
“Well done everyone” grouper began to shout
“It’s not over yet” exclaimed Mother as the barracuda came about

The barracuda were angry and bared their sharp teeth
“We are not done with you, you can’t hide in the reef”
The barracuda started to circle and had Mother in view
Freddie screamed “Sam, what on earth can we do?”

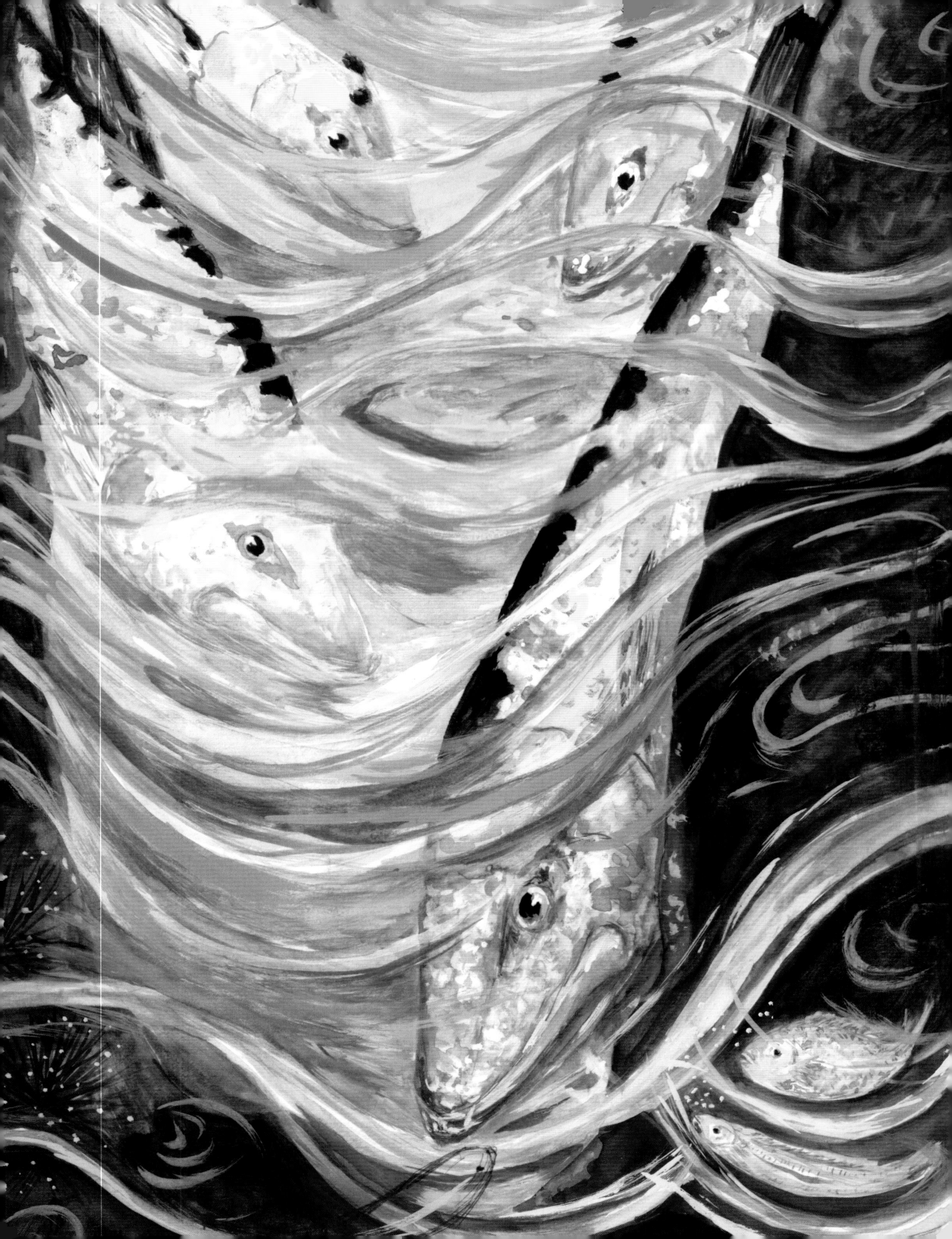

Just then a ray moved in with its long barbed tail
It stung the barracuda who began to wail
The barracuda wriggled and tried to get free
“Come on” said the sea urchins “bump into me”

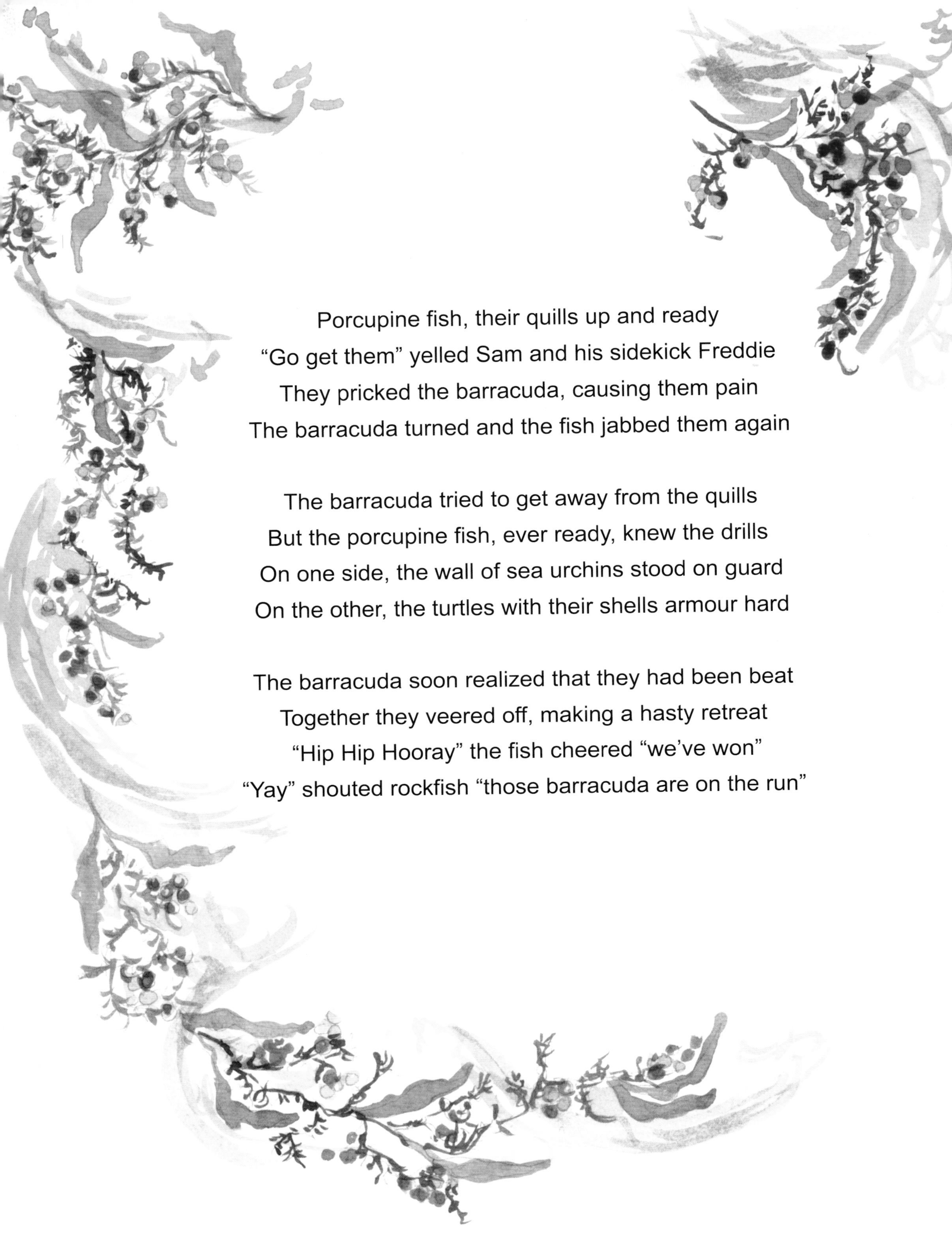

Porcupine fish, their quills up and ready
“Go get them” yelled Sam and his sidekick Freddie
They pricked the barracuda, causing them pain
The barracuda turned and the fish jabbed them again

The barracuda tried to get away from the quills
But the porcupine fish, ever ready, knew the drills
On one side, the wall of sea urchins stood on guard
On the other, the turtles with their shells armour hard

The barracuda soon realized that they had been beat
Together they veered off, making a hasty retreat
“Hip Hip Hooray” the fish cheered “we’ve won”
“Yay” shouted rockfish “those barracuda are on the run”

Everyone began to praise and thank Freddie and Sam
For all of their courage and their brilliant plan
They had learned that in the sea as on land
We all need our friends to lend a hand

Now every year they celebrate their greatest victory
The battle of the barracuda recorded in history
Urchins, rays, squid and turtles playing their part
Saving North Rock so dear to their heart

But now we must bid farewell to North Rock's glory
You may have guessed, this is the end of our story.

The cast of characters

Barracuda

Barracuda are often to be found around shallow bays which is why they can be seen at North Rock. They belong to the *Sphyraena* family. Barracuda are known to sneak up from behind and can appear scary as their mouths are big and they have lots of teeth. They are a curious fish and often will come quite close. Barracuda can grow as big as six feet and if you should happen to see one with its mouth open and full of sharp teeth it is easy to see why you might be frightened. In fact they are not really as scary as people make them out to be. It is this curiosity and their menacing looks which cause the fright.

Cahow

The cahow or Bermuda petrel (*ptereodroma cahow*) is Bermuda's National Bird. Once thought to be extinct, it has been brought back by dedicated conservationists but is still on the endangered list. The cahow spends most of its time on the open ocean and feeds on small squid, shrimp and fish.

Conch

The conch (*Strombus gigas*) is a large sea snail. They are native to Bermuda and have been "overfished" which has placed them on the endangered list of marine molluscs. They eat algae and marine plants and live in and around the sandy shore. The conch lays hundreds of thousands of eggs which float around for about five days before settling to the sandy sea bed. Man is one of the conch's enemies as their meat is a delicacy. Conchs can live for forty years.

Cow Polly

The cow polly's other name is the sergeant major damselfish (*Abudefduf saxatilis*). These fish eat seaweed and seamat from coral reefs. Their vibrant stripes give them a very striking appearance. The cow polly is an inquisitive little fish and will come close to you and even try and clean your legs by taking little "nips". If you should be swimming or snorkeling at North Rock you will soon notice some of these fish following you around.

Eel

Moray eels (*Muraenidae*) look like a snake but really are fish. They hunt at night and although they cannot see or hear well have a keen sense of smell and movement. The main predators of the eel are the grouper, rockfish and barracuda. They can tie their bodies in knots and by doing this anchor themselves to their hiding spot and wait for an unsuspecting meal like a small fish to swim by.

Flamingo tongued snail

These snails (*Cyphoma gibbosum*) are members of the mollusc family. They attach themselves to sea fans and corals and eat the plankton which grows there.

Freddie

Freddie is a blue headed wrasse (*Thalassoma bifasciatum*). These fish are found in reefs and shallow areas in the Western Atlantic Ocean, including Bermuda. They grow to approximately 9.8 inches. They are fearless and can be aggressive but seem to get on well with most fish.

Grunt

Grunts (*Haemulidae sciurus*) can be found under coral heads and feed on crabs and shrimp at night. They have an uncanny way of knowing where to go and how to get there. When caught they make a loud grunting noise; hence their name.

Jellyfish

Jellyfish (*Scyphozoan*) are extremely old and are reputed to have existed more than 650 million years ago, predating dinosaurs by almost 400 million years. They don't have a brain and it is still not entirely understood how they navigate their way around or find food. Even though they are called jellyfish they are not fish. A group of jellyfish are called a bloom swarm or smack. They are a delicacy for turtles and whales.

Octopus

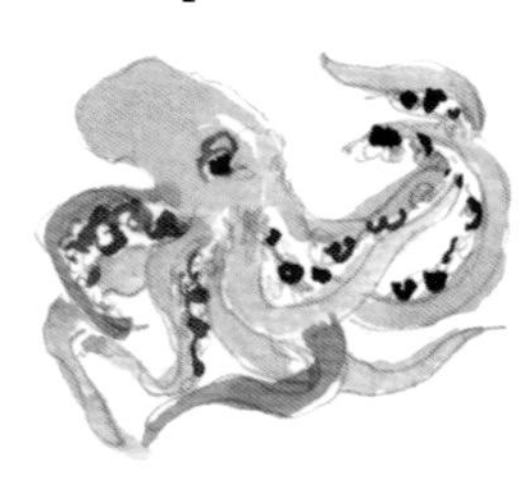

The octopus (*Cephalopod mollusk of the order octopoda*) has a soft body with a well developed brain and is very intelligent. The octopus, with eyes on each side of its head, has brilliant eyesight which is very useful as the octopus is completely deaf. The reason it is called octopus is because it has eight tentacles and "octo" means eight. The octopus communicates while changing colour and when it gets really frightened it turns white. The octopus can also regenerate itself so if it loses one of its tentacles it will grow back.

Parrot fish

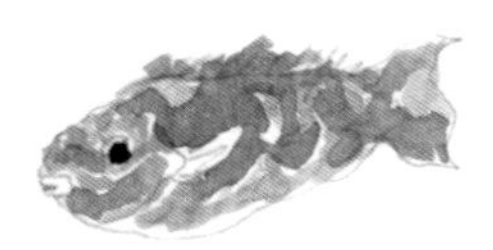

The parrot fish is related to the wrasses and is part of the *Scarinae* family. "Like underwater dentists" parrot fish help to clean the reef. At night, they sleep in caves and cover their bodies with a slimy case or bubble much like pajamas so if the bubble gets bumped or jostled the fish wake up and flee before it's too late. The parrot fish's mouth is fused into a beak and as they are so colourful its easy to see why they are called parrot fish.

Porcupine fish

The porcupine fish is part of the balloon fish family (*Diodon hystrix*). By swallowing water the porcupine fish can puff itself up to become the size of a large ball. When its quills, which are lethal, are "open" it can be mistaken for a sea urchin. The porcupine fish has teeth that never stop growing so they must chew on hard rocks and coral to keep them at a reasonable size. They are able to squirt water from their mouths and this helps dislodge bugs and other goodies from the corals.

Pudding wife

The pudding wife (*Halichoeres radiates*) is a rainbow coloured fish and is a member of the wrasse family, making it Freddie's cousin. It spends its days hunting for little snails hiding under rocks on the sandy shore.

Ray

Rays (*Dasyatidae*) are also very old and have existed for millions of years. They are very graceful and glide effortlessly through the water; they are fast and can even jump large distances. They are filter feeders much like the whale. Rays are related to sharks.

Rockfish and Grouper

These fish are from the same family (*Epinephelus striatus*). They grow to a considerable size and have huge mouths which they open by dropping their lower jaw, giving these fish a "downturned grin". They swim alone and live a rather solitary existence.

Sam

Sam is a Bermuda bream (*Diplodus bermudensis*) often described as a "run of the mill" fish. Not particularly beautiful, this little fish has the honour of being one of Bermuda's endemic species which means it is not found anywhere else in the world.

Sea Fan

Sea fans (*Gorgonians*) have eight arms or tentacles unlike their cousins, the corals, who have six arms. The arms or tentacles are attached to polyps and at night the polyps open like a flower and catch little crustaceans that have come out of hiding. The sea fans fasten themselves to the hard coral or sea bed and they prefer to be on the outer side of the reef where they have the best chance of catching food.

Sea horse

Seahorses (*Hippocampus*) are actually fish but are poor swimmers.They swim upright and use their tails to wrap themselves around the sea grass so that they do not get swept away. A female seahorse lays her eggs in the male pouch. The males carry the eggs until the baby seahorses are born, sometimes as many as fifteen hundred! Seahorses have a crown on their heads which is very much like the human finger print. They can change colour like a chameleon so as to blend in with their surroundings and avoid being eaten. Seahorses are on the endangered list.

Sea Urchin

Sea urchins (*Echinoidea*) are some of the oldest animals found on earth, even though they live underwater. They have a mass of spines covering their body and often will carry little shells or pieces of rocks, giving them a different appearance. Sea urchins do not have a brain and instead have a nerve ring which they use to move their tubed feet. They scrape algae off the rocks with their teeth.

Squid

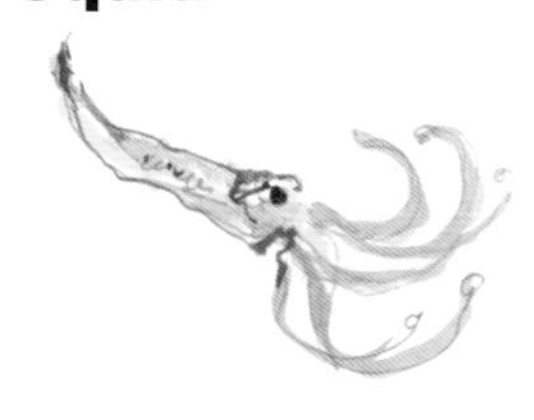

Squid are a type of marine cephalopod with ten limbs. They have a rocket shaped body which allows them to move quite quickly through the water. Squid never close their eyes as they don't have any eyelids. They squirt ink when they are threatened so as to conceal their whereabouts from their enemies.

Trumpet fish

Trumpet fish (*Aulostomus maculatus*) often hide upside down in soft coral. They have a large mouth which opens in a shape just like that of a trumpet. Sometimes a group of trumpet fish will stand to attention and then move off all together, giving the appearance of a much bigger fish.

Turtle

Sea turtles (*Chelonioidea*) eat sea grass and seaweed. About a million years ago they separated from their cousins the land turtles. The biggest difference, apart from living in water, is that sea turtles cannot retract their head and feet into their shell like their land cousins can. Sea turtles are on the endangered list and there are many ongoing conservation projects which protect the areas where they lay their eggs. They have two large paddle like feet which allows them to swim quickly. Sea turtles spend most of their time in the water except when they come ashore to lay their eggs. They tend to prefer the shallower waters.

About the Author and Illustrator

Debbie Jones

I loved reading stories to my three children when they were little and I wrote so many that never made it beyond the bits of paper they were written on. It was when, as a family, we snorkeled at North Rock that I became inspired to write about the little fish that live there. My best friend Jodie Tucker is an artist and many of her paintings were fish. When I read her the first story she agreed to illustrate it and for those of you who have read the first Fish Tales you know what a wonderful artist she is. That was seventeen years ago! Hope you enjoy the next Fish Tales - Battle of the Barracuda. This book has taken a few years to get to the point where it could be published. It has only been possible because of the patience of my husband who has read and reread it more than a few times. Writing is something I love to do in my spare time when I am not working as a diabetes educator in Bermuda.

Jodie Elizabeth Tucker

The strongest influence on my work as an artist has remained the place of my birth, the Island of Bermuda. I grew up next to Hungry Bay which held many adventures and I remember sitting on the dock watching all manner of fishes in the shallow clear waters. I drew on these childhood memories when asked to illustrate Fish Tales by my dear friend Debbie Jones. It made a perfect partnership, Debbie writing her delightful poems of the adventures of two fish, Freddie and Sam and inspired by her favourite place the offshore reef of North Rock, together with my illustrations of the various species of life under the sea.